# Look at the Painting

## Written by Jillian Powell

# Look at the girl.

2

# Look at the dog.

# Look at the man.

Look at his hat.

# Look at the table.

# Look at the fruit.

⑦

# Look at the water.

# Look at the boat.

Look at the painting.

# Look for...

the gloves

the tree

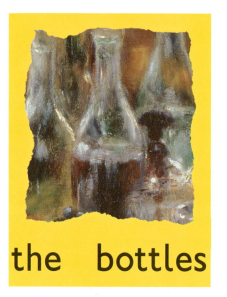

the bottles

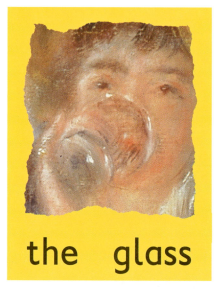

the glass